TODAY'S WORK-PLAY BOOKS

By

Arthur I. Gates

Miriam Blanton Huber

Celeste Comegys Peardon

Frank Seely Salisbury

ON OUR WAY

MY WORK-PLAY BOOK for COME AND RIDE

COME AND RIDE

THIS IS FUN

MY WORK-PLAY BOOK for TAGS AND TWINKLE

TAGS AND TWINKLE

MY WORK-PLAY BOOK for GOOD TIMES ON OUR STREET

GOOD TIMES ON OUR STREET

MY WORK-PLAY BOOK for FRIENDS AND WORKERS

FRIENDS AND WORKERS

MY WORK-PLAY BOOK for ON LONGER TRAILS

ON LONGER TRAILS

(Continuing This Series)

THE NEW WORK-PLAY BOOKS

By

Arthur I. Gates

Jean Ayer

PREPARATORY BOOK to accompany LET'S LOOK AROUND

LET'S LOOK AROUND

PREPARATORY BOOK to accompany LET'S TRAVEL ON

LET'S TRAVEL ON

PREPARATORY BOOK to accompany LET'S GO AHEAD

LET'S GO AHEAD

Tags and Twinkle

TODAY'S WORK-PLAY BOOKS

GATES · HUBER · PEARDON · SALISBURY

The Macmillan Company

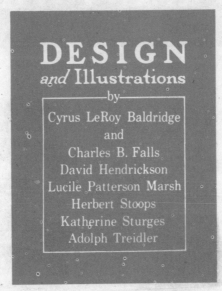

DESIGN
and Illustrations
——by——
Cyrus LeRoy Baldridge
and
Charles B. Falls
David Hendrickson
Lucile Patterson Marsh
Herbert Stoops
Katherine Sturges
Adolph Treidler

A revision of *Jim and Judy*, copyright, 1939, by The
Macmillan Company; *Jim and Judy* a revision of *Peter
and Peggy*, copyright, 1930, by Arthur I. Gates and
Miriam Blanton Huber.

Stories

Jim and Judy

This is Jim.

This is Judy.

This is Tags.

"Here, Tags!" said Jim.
"Come here, Tags!"

5

"Look, Judy!" said Jim.
"Look at Tags!"

6

ghed.

dy.

Judy la   and lau

"This is fun!" said Ju

The Toys

dy," said Jim.

the toys.

e and get the toys."

8

"Toys! Toys! Toys!" said Judy.
"Look at the toys!"

"Here, Tags!" said Jim.
"Come and ride.
Ride, ride, ride!"

10

A Toy Farm

"Jim," said Judy.
"Make a farm.
Make a toy farm.
I like farms."

"I will make a farm," said Jim.
"I will make a toy farm."

"We went to a farm," said Judy.
"A farm is fun.
I will like a toy farm."

"Look, Judy," said Jim.
"Here is a farmer.
Here is a wagon.
Look at the wagon."

"Look at the calf," said Jim.

"A calf likes hay," said Judy.
"I will get hay for the calf."

"Here comes Father," said Jim.
"Look, Father.
Look at the toy farm."

"Jim," said Father.
"I like the toy farm.
I like the wagon.
Make the wagon red.
I like a red wagon."

"I will," said Jim.
"I will make the wagon red."

"I like this farm," said Judy.
"I like the farmer.
I like the calf.
I like the red wagon.
A toy farm is fun."

Birthday Surprises

Judy and Mother

"Mother! Mother!" said Judy.
"Tomorrow is Jim's birthday!"

"A birthday is fun," said Mother.

"Tomorrow!" said Judy.
"Tomorrow is Jim's birthday!"

"Mother," said Judy.
"I will get a surprise for Jim."

"Make a surprise," said Mother.
"Make a birthday surprise."

"Come, Mother," said Judy.
"We will make a wagon for Jim.
Jim likes wagons."

A Surprise for Jim

"Look, Judy," said Mother.
"Here is a box.
A box will make a wagon."

"I like this box," said Judy.
"This box will make a wagon."

"A surprise is fun," said Mother.
"Jim will like this surprise."

Judy laughed and laughed.
"I like birthdays," said Judy.

"Judy," said Mother.
"We will go and get wheels.
Wheels for the wagon!"

"Here we go," said Judy.
"Here we go to get the wheels.
Wheels! Wheels!
Wheels for Jim's wagon!"

Mother laughed at Judy.

"Look, Judy," said Mother.
"The wheels go on the box.
This will make a wagon."

"Wheels on a box!" said Judy.
"Wheels on a box!
We will make a wagon!
A wagon for Jim's birthday!"

The Red Wagon

"Look, Mother," said Judy.
"I will make the wagon red.
Jim will like a red wagon."

"Judy," said Mother.
"Make the wheels red.
Jim will like red wheels."

"Red wheels!" said Judy.
"Red wheels on a red wagon!
Jim will like this wagon."

"I like it," said Mother.
"Father will like it.
And Jim will like it."

"This wagon will go," said Judy.
"It will go and go and go!"

Tags Is Red

"Look at the wagon!" said Judy.
"The wagon can go!
Jim can make the wagon go."

"Jim will like it," said Mother.
"Jim will like this surprise."

"Look, Tags!" said Judy.
"Look at the wagon.
It is a surprise for Jim.
Tomorrow is Jim's birthday."

Tags went to the wagon.
Tags got into the wagon.

"Mother! Mother!" said Judy.
"Look at Tags!
Tags got into the wagon!
Tags got into Jim's wagon!"

"Get out, Tags!" said Mother.
"Get out of the wagon!
This is Jim's wagon!"

Tags got out of the wagon.
Judy laughed and laughed.
Mother laughed and laughed.

"Look at Tags!" said Judy.
"Tags is red!"

Tags ran.
Judy ran.

"Tags! Tags!" said Judy.
"Come here, Tags!"

Tags ran and ran.
Judy ran and ran.

"Here, Tags!" said Judy.
"Red Tags!"

A Wagon for Jim

"Look at Tags!" said Judy.
Mother laughed.

"Judy," said Mother.
"Tags likes the red wagon."

"It is for Jim," said Judy.
"It is for Jim's birthday.
Tags can not have the wagon."

"Judy," said Mother.
"Jim will like the surprise.
Jim will have a happy birthday."

"We will have fun," said Judy.
"We will have fun tomorrow.
Happy birthday to Jim!
I like birthdays."

"Come, Tags," said Mother.
"The wagon is for Jim.
It is a surprise for Jim.
It is not for Tags."

Happy Birthday

"Happy birthday!" said Mother.
"Happy birthday, Jim!"

"Happy birthday!" said Father.

"Happy birthday!" said Judy.

"Thank you, Mother," said Jim.
"Thank you, Father.
Thank you, Judy."

"Jim," said Judy.
"I have a surprise for you.
It is a birthday surprise."

"What is it?" said Jim.
"What is the surprise?"

"You will see," said Judy.
"You will see what it is."

"I like surprises," said Jim.
"Did you make the surprise?
Did you make it, Judy?"

"Yes, I did," said Judy.
"Mother and I did.
You will like the surprise."

"What is it, Judy?" said Jim.
"What is the surprise?"

"Come and see, Jim," said Judy.
"Come and see the surprise."

"Oh! Oh! Oh!" said Jim.
"I like this surprise!
Thank you, Judy.
Thank you."

"Look at the wheels," said Judy.

"Yes," said Jim.
"See the red wheels!
This wagon can go.
Oh, I like a red wagon!"

"Tags! Oh, Tags!" said Jim.
"See what I have!
A red wagon!
Come and ride, Tags."

Tags got into the wagon.

"Here we go," said Jim.
"Ride, Tags, ride!"

A Birthday Ride

"Get in, Jim," said Father.
"Get in, Judy.
We will go for a ride.
This is a birthday ride."

"Oh, Father!" said Jim.
"This is fun!
I like a birthday ride.
It is fun to have a birthday."

"Here we go!" said Judy.
"Here we go for a birthday ride!"

Birthday Fun

"Oh, Judy!" said Jim.
"See the boys and girls!"

"It is a surprise," said Judy.
"Mother did it.
It is a surprise for you."

"Oh, Jim!" said the boys and girls.
"Happy birthday to you!
Happy birthday to you!"

"Thank you," said Jim.
"Thank you."

The boys and girls played.
Jim and Judy played.

"Oh! Oh! Oh!" said Jim.
"This is fun!
It is fun to have a surprise.
It is fun to have a birthday."

"Look, look!" said Judy.
"Oh, this is fun."

The boys and girls laughed.
Jim laughed and laughed.

"Here is Mother," said Judy.

"Come," said Mother.
"Come, boys and girls.
Come, Jim and Judy."

The Birthday Cake

"Look at the cake!" said the girls.
"See the birthday cake!"

"Birthday cake!" said the boys.
"See Jim's birthday cake!"

"Oh, Tags!" said Judy.
"You can not have the cake.
It is for the boys and girls."

"This is fun!" said the girls.

"We like cake," said the boys.
"We like Jim's birthday cake!"

"Good-by," said the boys.
"Happy birthday, Jim!"

"Good-by," said the girls.
"Happy birthday, Jim!"

"Thank you," said Jim.
"Good-by."

"Good-by," said Judy.

Airplanes

45

Fun with Tags

"Oh, Jim!" said Judy.
"What can we do?"

"Judy," said Jim.
"I know what we can do.
We can have fun with Tags."

"Here, Tags!" said Jim.
"Come here, Tags!"

Tags ran to Jim.

"Get it, Tags!" said Jim.
"I know you can do it.
Go and get it, Tags!"

Away went Tags.

Jim played with Tags.
They ran and played.
They played and played.

"Oh, Jim!" said Judy.
"I want to have fun with Tags."

"Yes, Judy," said Jim.
"Come and have fun."

"Here, Tags!" said Judy.
"Go and get it!
I want you to get it.
I know you can do it."

Away went Tags.

Jim and Judy laughed.
They laughed and laughed.

Tags ran and ran.
Tags did get it.

The Big Airplanes

"Look, Judy, look!" said Jim.
"See the big airplanes!"

"Oh! Oh! Oh!" said Judy.
"See the big airplanes go up.
Up, up, up they go!"

"This is fun," said Jim.
"Oh, yes!" said Judy.
"It is fun to look at airplanes."

"Judy," said Jim.
"I want to go up.
I want to ride in airplanes."

"Yes, Jim," said Judy.
"I want to ride in airplanes.'

"We will," said Jim.
"I know we will.
We will ride in airplanes."

The Toy Airplane

"I like airplanes," said Jim.
"I can make a toy airplane."

"Oh, yes!" said Judy.
"You can make a toy airplane!"

Jim did make a toy airplane.
He painted the toy airplane.
He painted it red.

"Here it is, Judy," said Jim.
"I painted it red."

"Look, Judy, look!" said Jim.
"See the toy airplane go up!"

Up, up went the toy airplane.
Down, down it went.

Tags ran to get it.

"No! No! No!" said Jim.
"Get away, Tags!
You can not have
the toy airplane!"

"Here is Father," said Judy.

"Oh, Father!" said Jim.
"I have a toy airplane."

"Did you make it?" said Father.

"Yes, Father," said Jim.
"I did make it.
I painted it red.
I want you to see it.
It is a good airplane."

"Yes, Father," said Judy.
"It is a good toy airplane."

"Jim," said Father.
"It is a good toy airplane.
Will it go up?"

"Yes, Father," said Jim.
"It will go up.
It will come down, too."

"Father," said Judy.
"Tags wants the toy airplane."

"No, Tags," said Father.
"You can not have it."

"Father," said Jim.
"Make the toy airplane go up.
Make it go up and up and up!"

"I will," said Father.
"Look, Jim and Judy.
See it go up!"

Up went the toy airplane.
It went up and up.

"See it go!" said Jim.
"See it go up!"

The toy airplane went down, too.
Down, down it went.

Tags ran to get the toy airplane.
"No, no, Tags!" said Jim.

Father laughed and laughed.
"This is fun for Tags," he said.
"This is fun for Jim and Judy.
It is fun for Father, too."

Surprises

Father went into the house.
Judy went into the house.
Tags went into the house, too.

"Come, Jim," said Mother.

"Oh, Mother!" said Jim.
"We can make the airplane go!
We can make it go up and up!"

Father laughed.
"It is a good airplane," he said.

"Judy," said Mother.
"I have a surprise."

"What is it, Mother?" said Judy.
"Is it something to eat?"

"Yes," said Mother.
"It is something to eat.
It is a cake."

"Thank you, Mother!" said Judy.

"We like cake," said Father.

"Jim and Judy," said Father.
"I have a surprise, too."

"What is it?" said Jim.
"Is it something to eat?"
"No, Jim," said Father.
"It is not something to eat."

Father laughed.
"Do you like airplanes?" he said.
"Oh, yes!" said Jim and Judy.

"Jim and Judy," said Father.
"The surprise is a ride.
It is a ride in a big airplane."

"Oh! Oh!" said Jim and Judy.
"This is a good surprise!"

"We will go tomorrow,"
said Father.
"We will ride in a big airplane."

"Will Tags go, too?" said Jim.
"Yes, Jim," said Father.
"Tags will go, too."

"Tomorrow!" said Jim and Judy.
"Tomorrow we will ride
in a big airplane!"

The Airplane Ride

"Look!" said Jim.
"Look at the airplanes!"

"Father!" said Jim.
"The airplanes are big.
Big, big airplanes!"

"Yes, Jim," said Father.
They are big airplanes."

"Oh, Mother!" said Judy.
"I like the big airplanes!"

"Judy," said Mother.
"Do you want to ride?"

"Oh, yes, Mother!" said Judy.

"Mother," said Father.
"See this white airplane.
Do you like this airplane?"

"Oh, yes!" said Mother.

"I know the pilot," said Father.
"We can ride
in this white airplane."

"Good!" said Mother.

A man got out of the airplane.
"He is the pilot," said Father.

The pilot went to Father.

"It is good to see you,"
said the pilot.
"Do you want to ride?"

"Oh, yes!" said Father.
"We do want to ride!"

"Come," said the pilot.

"Come, Mother," said Father.
"This man is a good pilot."

The pilot got into the airplane.
Mother and Father got in.
Jim and Judy got in.
Tags got into the airplane, too.

"Here we go!" said Jim.
"We are going for a ride!
A ride in a big white airplane!"
"Oh, this is fun!" said Judy.

In the Airplane

Up, up, up went the airplane.

"Oh, Jim!" said Judy.
"We are going up!"

"Yes, we are," said Jim.
"Look, Judy!
Look down!"

"I see houses," said Judy.
"They look little!"

"Yes, they do," said Jim.
"All the houses look little."

"I see a farm," said Judy.
"I can see the farm house.
It is a white farm house."

"Judy," said Mother.
"Can you see the farmer?"

Judy laughed.
"No, no!" said Judy.
"I can not see the farmer.
But I know he is on the farm."

"I see a wagon," said Jim.
"I know it is a hay wagon."

"Jim," said Judy.
"Can you see a calf?"

Jim laughed.
"No, no!" he said.
"I can not see a calf.
A calf is too little.
But I know it is on the farm."

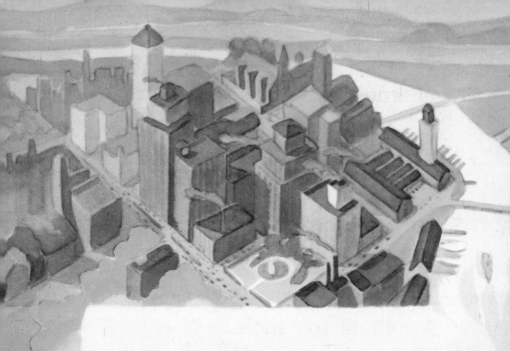

"Look, Jim!" said Father.
"Look down at the city."

"Oh! Oh! Oh!" said Jim.
"The city looks big!"

"It is big," said Father.
"It is a big city."

"Look, Judy!" said Jim.
"Look at the big city."

Jim and Judy looked down.
Mother looked down, too.
They saw the big city.
They saw houses and houses.

"I like this city," said Jim.

"Yes, Jim," said Judy.
"I like this city, too."

71

Jim looked down at the city.
"I can see houses in the city,"
he said.

Judy looked down at the city.
"Jim," she said.
"Can you see boys and girls?"

Jim laughed.
"No, no!" he said.
"I can not see boys and girls."

"I like this ride," said Mother.
"It is a good ride."

"Yes, it is," said Father.
"But look!
We are going down!"

"Oh, Father!" said Jim.
"Are we going down?
I want to go on and on and on!"

Father laughed.
"Jim likes to ride," he said.
"We all like to ride," said Mother.

Down, down went the airplane.
The big white airplane
went down, down, down.

The pilot got out of the airplane.
Father and Mother got out.
Jim and Judy got out, too.

"Oh! Oh!" said Jim and Judy.
"We like to ride
in a big airplane!"

74

Jim went to the pilot.

"Thank you for the ride,"
said Jim.

"Thank you for the ride,"
said Judy.

"It was fun," said the pilot.

"It was a good ride,"
said Father.

Where Is Tags?

"Come, Judy," said Father.
"We will go home."

"Come, Jim," said Mother.
"We will go home."

"Where is Tags?" said Jim.
"Where is Tags?" said Judy.
"Where is Tags?"
they all said.

76

"Here, Tags!" said Jim.
"Come here, Tags!"

But Tags did not come.

"Jim," said Father.
"Is he in the airplane?"

"I will see," said the pilot.
"I will look in the airplane."

The pilot went into the airplane.

77

The pilot looked in the airplane.
He did not see Tags.

"No," said the pilot.
"He is not in the airplane."

"Where is he?" said Jim.
"Where is he?" said Judy.
"Where is he?" they all said.

"Bow-wow! Bow-wow!"

It was Tags.

"Bow-wow!" said Tags.
"Bow-wow! Bow-wow!"

"Oh, Judy!" said Jim.
"Tags is in the airplane!
Come here, Tags, come here!"

Jim ran into the airplane.
Judy ran into the airplane.

There was Tags!
There was a cat, too!
A little white cat in the airplane!

"Tags!" said Jim.
"Where did you get this cat?"

"Bow-wow!" said Tags.

"I know!" said Judy.
"She ran into the airplane.
Tags ran into the airplane, too."

"Bow-wow! Bow-wow!" said Tags.

"I like cats," said Judy.
"I want a little white cat.
Come here, little cat, come here!"

Twinkle, the Cat

"Oh, Mother!" said Judy.
"See the little white cat!"

"Judy," said Mother.
"Where did you get this cat?"

"In the airplane!" said Judy.
"She ran into the airplane.
Tags ran into the airplane, too.
Jim and I went to get Tags.
There was the cat with Tags
in the airplane!"

"Judy," said the pilot.
"It is not my cat.
The little cat wants a home.
Do you want the cat?"

"Oh, yes, yes!" said Judy.

Judy looked at Mother.
Mother laughed.
"Yes, Judy," said Mother.

"Thank you, Mother," said Judy.
"I will call the cat 'Twinkle.'
Twinkle, my little white cat!"

Jim and Judy said "Good-by"
to the pilot.

"Thank you for the ride,"
said Jim.

"Thank you for my cat,"
said Judy.

"Twinkle is my airplane cat."

"Good-by," said Mother.

"Look, Twinkle!" said Jim.
"Here we go home!"

"Bow-wow!" said Tags.

Fun at the Farm

The Train Ride

"Here we go!" said Jim and Judy.
"Here we go to the farm!"

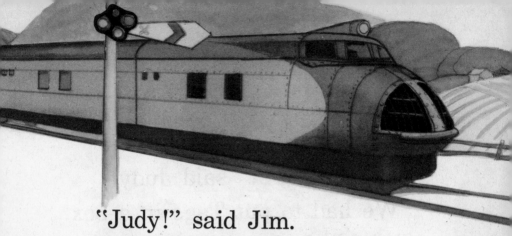

"Judy!" said Jim.
"Put Twinkle in the box!
I put Tags in a box.
Twinkle will have to ride
in a box on the train."

"Yes! Yes!" said Judy.
"Get in the box, Twinkle!
You will have to ride
in a box on the train."

She put Twinkle in the box.

Away went the train.
Away went Jim and Judy.

Jim and Judy got out
of the train.
They saw the farmer.

"Here we are!" said Judy.
"We had to put Tags in a box.
Twinkle is in a box, too.
I call my cat 'Twinkle.'"

The farmer laughed.
He took Jim and Judy
to the farm.
He took Tags and Twinkle, too.

The Cows

The farmer took Jim and Judy
to the barn.

"I want you to see my barn,"
he said.

"I want you to see my cows."

"Look at the cows!" said Jim.

"Come into the barn,"
said the farmer.
"I will get something
for the cows to eat."

Jim and Judy went
into the barn.
Tags and Twinkle went, too.

"Oh, Jim!" said Judy.
"Call Tags! Call Tags!
Some of the cows
do not like Tags."

"Here, Tags!" said Jim.
"Go to the house, Tags!"

Tags did not want to go.
But he had to go.

The Hens

"Do you want to see my hens?"
said the farmer.

"Oh, yes!" said Judy.

The farmer took Jim and Judy
to the hen house.
They saw white hens.
They saw black hens.

"Look at all the big hens!"
said Judy.

"Jim and Judy," said the farmer.
"Will you get the eggs for me?"

"Yes, we will," said Jim and Judy.
"We like to get the eggs."

"Thank you," said the farmer.
"Get all the eggs for me."

Jim looked for eggs.
Judy looked for eggs.

"Here they are," said Jim.
"Here are some eggs."

"Look, Jim!" said Judy.
"Look at the black rooster!"

Jim looked at the rooster.
"Is this the biggest rooster
on the farm?" he said.

"This is my biggest rooster,"
said the farmer.

Jim laughed at the rooster.
"You are a big rooster!" he said.
"I like you, big black rooster."

Twinkle and the Rooster

The rooster saw Twinkle.
He did not like
this little white animal.
He said, "Cock-a-doodle-doo!
I do not like you!"

Twinkle looked at the rooster.
"I do not like you!" she said.

She ran at the black rooster.
The black rooster ran.
Twinkle ran, too.

Up on the hen house
went the black rooster.
He looked down at Twinkle.

He said, "Cock-a-doodle-doo!
I do not like you!
But you can not get me!
I am the biggest rooster
on the farm!
You can not get me!
Cock-a-doodle-doo!
Cock-a-doodle-doo!"

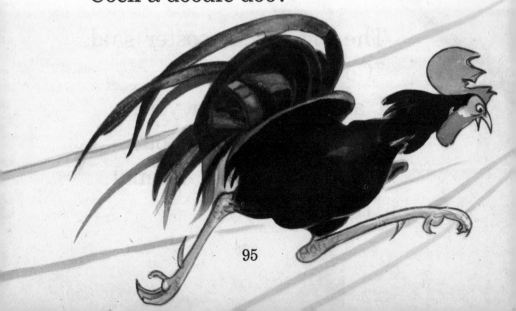

95

The big black rooster said,
"Cock-a-doodle-doo!
I am bigger than you!
I am bigger than you!
I am the biggest animal
on the farm!"

The black rooster said,
"Cock-a-doodle-doo!
I am bigger than you!
I am bigger than the hens!
I am bigger than the calf!
I am bigger than
the black and white cow!
I am the biggest animal
on the farm!
Cock-a-doodle-doo!
Cock-a-doodle-doo!"

Jim laughed at the rooster.
Judy laughed at him, too.

"Jim and Judy," said the farmer.
"The rooster went to the city."

"Did he?" said Jim and Judy.
"Did he go to the city?"

"Yes, he did," said the farmer.

The farmer laughed.
"Did I tell you the story
of my black rooster?" he said.

"No," said Judy.
"You did not tell the story."

"Tell it! Tell it!" said Jim.
"I like a good story."

"I will tell you the story,"
said the farmer.
"Come into the house,
and I will tell the story."

"A story is fun!" said Judy.

This is the story
of the black rooster.

The Story of the
Black Rooster

Little Chickens

Mother Hen was happy.
She had a home on the farm.
She had some little chickens.

"Look! Look!" she said.
"I have little yellow chickens.
I have a little black rooster.
We have a good home.
Look! Look! Look!"

Mother Hen was happy
with the little chickens.

There was a man in the city.
He had a pet store.

"I know what I will do,"
said the man.
"I will get some little chickens.
I will put some little chickens
in my pet store.
Boys and girls like chickens.
They like yellow chickens."

A letter came to the farmer.

The letter said, "Do you have
some little chickens?

I want some yellow chickens.

I want to put the chickens
in my pet store.

Boys and girls like chickens."

The farmer went to the barn.

"Come here, little chickens,"
he said.

"You are going away.

You are going to the city.

You are going to a pet store
in the city.

Boys and girls will look at you.

They like little chickens."

"Chickens," said the farmer.
"I have a box for you.
I will put you in the box.
You will ride in the box
to the city."

The farmer laughed.
"Little black rooster," he said.
"You can not go to the city.
The man wants yellow chickens.
You are not a yellow chicken.
You can not go to the city."

"Peep! Peep!" said the rooster.
"I want to go to the city, too."

The farmer put the chickens
into the box.
Then he went away.

The little black rooster
came up to the box.
"Peep! Peep! Peep!" he said.
"I want to go to the city
with the little yellow chickens."

Then the farmer's wife came.
She saw the little black rooster.

"Oh!" said the farmer's wife.
"The little black rooster
got out of the box.
I will put him in."

Into the box
went the little black rooster.
"Peep! Peep! Peep!" he said.
"I am going to the city, too.
Peep! Peep! Peep!"

106

The City

The farmer took the box
to the train.
The little black rooster
was in the box.

Away went the train.
Away went the chickens.
Away went the black rooster.

"Here I go!" said the rooster.
"I am going to the city now!"

The little rooster was happy.
Now he was going to the city.

The train came to the city.
The black rooster looked out.

There was no farm now.
There was no barn.
There was no farmer.
There was no farmer's wife.

He saw big stores.
He saw big houses.
"Peep! Peep!" said the rooster.
"I am in the city now!"

The little chickens came
to the pet store.
The man took the chickens
out of the box.

"Look at this!" said the man.
"One black rooster!
My letter said yellow chickens.
I do not want a black rooster!"

The man put the yellow chickens
in the pet store.
He did not put the black rooster
in the store.

"Peep! Peep!" said the rooster.
The man laughed.
Then he put him
in the store, too.

Two Little Houses

The man had two little houses
in the pet store.
One little house was
for the chickens.
One little house was
for the rabbits.

The man had two gray rabbits.

"Here is something to eat, gray rabbits," he said.

"And here is something for you to eat, little chickens."

"Peep! Peep! Peep!" said the little chickens.

Peep! Peep!

The little yellow chickens
had all they wanted to eat.
But they wanted to go home.
They wanted to go home!

"Peep! Peep!" they said.
"We do not like the city.
We like the farm.
We want Mother Hen.
We want the farmer.
We want the farmer's wife.
We want to go home.
Peep! Peep! Peep!"

But the little black rooster said,
"I like the city.
We have a good house.
We have something to eat.
We can see the rabbits.
We can see the boys and girls.
I like the city."

In the Pet Store

Boys and girls came
to the pet store.
They looked at the little houses.
"Oh! Oh! Oh!" they said.
"See the little yellow chickens!"

Then the little yellow chickens
looked happy.

But no one looked at the rooster.
No one said,
"See the little black rooster!"
This was not what
the little rooster wanted.
He wanted the boys and girls
to look at him.

114

Two little girls came
to the pet store.

"Oh! Oh! Oh!" they said.
"There is one black rooster!
See the little black rooster!"

Then all the boys and girls said,
"See the little black rooster!"

Now the little black rooster
was happy.
"Peep! Peep! Peep!" he said.

Two little boys came
to the pet store.
"See the little chickens!"
they said.
"We want some chickens.
We want the yellow chickens."

The two little boys took
all the yellow chickens home.

Then the black rooster said,
"Peep! Peep! I want to go home.
I want to go home to the farm."

The Letter

A letter came to the man
in the pet store.

"Look at this!" said the man.
"The farmer's wife wants
the little black rooster.
She wants him
to come home!"

The man got a little box
for the black rooster.
He put the rooster in the box.
He took the box to the train.

"Good-by, little black rooster,"
he said.

Then the little black rooster
went home to the farmer's wife.

"Peep! Peep! Peep!" he said.
"I like the city.
But my home is on the farm."

The Black Rooster at Home

"Jim and Judy," said the farmer.
"This is the story
of the little black rooster."

"He is big now," said Jim.
"He is a big, big rooster now."

The big black rooster said,
"Cock-a-doodle-doo!
I am bigger than you!
I am bigger than the calf!
I am bigger than the cow!
I am the biggest animal
on the farm!
I went to the city!
Cock-a-doodle-doo!
Cock-a-doodle-doo!"

Fun at School

Going to School

"Oh, Jim!" said Judy.
"We are going to school!"
"Yes," said Jim.
"I want to go to school."

"I want to go to school, too,"
said Judy.

"We will like school,"
said Jim.

Mother went to school
with Jim and Judy.

"Miss White," said Mother.
"Here are Jim and Judy."

"How do you do, Judy?"
said Miss White.
"How do you do, Jim?"

"How do you do, Miss White?"
said Jim and Judy.

"Come, Jim and Judy,"
said Miss White.
"Come and see
all the boys and girls."

The Rabbit

The boys and girls at school
had a rabbit.

It was a gray rabbit.

The gray rabbit had
a little house at school.

It was a little blue house.

"He likes the blue house,"
said the boys and girls.

The boys and girls played
with the rabbit.

Judy played with the rabbit.
"I will call him 'Gray Rabbit,'"
she said.
"Come here, Gray Rabbit.
Here is something to eat."

Jim played with the rabbit, too.
"I like you, Gray Rabbit,"
he said.
"I like to play with you.
Here is something for you."

The Play House

The boys and girls said,
"We will make a play house.
We will put a roof
on the play house.
We will make a door, too."

They did make a play house.

They painted the house white.
They painted the roof red.
They painted the door blue.

"I like the little white house,"
said Jim.

"I like the little red roof
and the little blue door."

"I like it, too," said Miss White.

"But no one lives in it,"
said Judy.

"I want some one to come
and live in the little house."

128

"I know what we can do,"
said Jim.

"We can make up a story.
We can have a boy and girl
live in the little white house."

"Jim," said Miss White.
"Will you make up a story?"
"Yes, Miss White," said Jim.

"Oh, Jim!" said one of the boys.
"Put a dog in the story."
"Oh, Jim!" said a girl.
"Put a cat in the story, too."

"I like hens," said a boy.
"Put in a rooster, too.
We like rabbits.
And we like horses, too."

Then they all laughed.
"Oh, Jim!" they said.
"Make up a good story!"

"I will," said Jim.

Jim did make up a story.
It had a boy and a girl in it.
It had a dog in it, too.
There was a cat.
There was a rooster.
There was a hen.
There was a rabbit.
And there was a horse.

This is Jim's story.

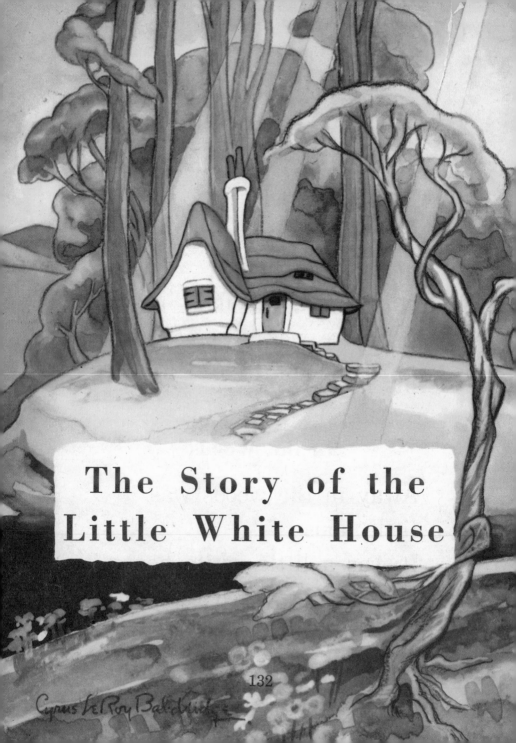

The Story of the
Little White House

Cyrus LeRoy Baldridge

In the Woods

Away in the woods was
a little house.
It was a little white house.
It had a little red roof
and a little blue door.

The little house was not happy.

"No one lives in me!"
said the little white house.
"No one lives in me!
I want some one to come
and live in me!"

The Boy and the Girl

A little boy and a little girl
had no home.

The little boy was not happy.

The little girl was not happy.

"We have no home!"
they said.

"We want a home!

We want a home!"

"Come," said Little Boy.

"We will find a home."

Black Dog

Little Boy and Little Girl
went to find a home.
They looked and looked.
They looked for a home.
But they did not find one.

Then they saw Black Dog.

"Black Dog," they said.
"We want to find a home."

"Go to the little white house
with the little red roof
and the little blue door,"
said Black Dog.

Little Boy said, "Where is
the little white house?"

"The little white house
with the little red roof
and the little blue door
is in the woods," said Black Dog.

"But I do not know
how to find it.

We must get Yellow Cat.
She knows how to find
the little white house."

So on went Little Boy
and Little Girl.
And on went Black Dog.

Yellow Cat

They saw Yellow Cat.

"How do you do, Yellow Cat?"
said Black Dog.

"Little Boy and Little Girl
have no home.

They want to find a home.

Yellow Cat, tell us how to find
the little white house
in the woods."

But Yellow Cat said,
"I do not know how to find
the little white house.
We must get Red Rooster.
He knows how to find
the little white house."

So on went Little Boy
and Little Girl.
And on went Black Dog
and Yellow Cat.

Red Rooster

They saw Red Rooster.

"How do you do, Red Rooster?"
said Yellow Cat.

"Little Boy and Little Girl
have no home.

They want to find a home.

Red Rooster, tell us
how to find the little white house
in the woods."

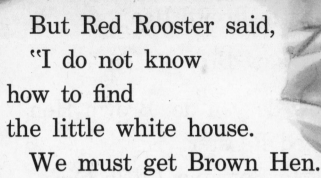

But Red Rooster said,
"I do not know
how to find
the little white house.
We must get Brown Hen.
She knows how to find
the little white house."

So on went Little Boy
and Little Girl.
And on went Black Dog
and Yellow Cat and Red Rooster.

Brown Hen

They saw Brown Hen.

"How do you do, Brown Hen?"
said Red Rooster.

"Little Boy and Little Girl
have no home.

They want to find a home.

Brown Hen, tell us how to find
the little white house
in the woods."

But Brown Hen said,
"I do not know
how to find
the little white house.
We must get Gray Rabbit.
He knows how to find
the little white house."

So on went Little Boy
and Little Girl.
On went Black Dog
and Yellow Cat.
And on went Red Rooster
and Brown Hen.

Gray Rabbit

They saw Gray Rabbit.

"How do you do, Gray Rabbit?"
said Brown Hen.

"Little Boy and Little Girl
have no home.

They want to find a home.

Gray Rabbit, tell us how to find
the little white house
in the woods."

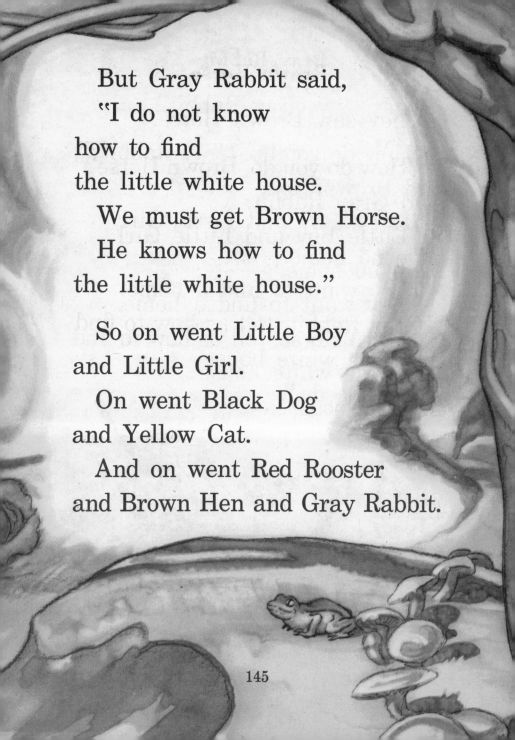

But Gray Rabbit said,
"I do not know
how to find
the little white house.
We must get Brown Horse.
He knows how to find
the little white house."

So on went Little Boy
and Little Girl.
On went Black Dog
and Yellow Cat.
And on went Red Rooster
and Brown Hen and Gray Rabbit.

Brown Horse

They saw Brown Horse.

"How do you do, Brown Horse?"
said Gray Rabbit.

"Little Boy and Little Girl
have no home.

They want to find a home.

Brown Horse, tell us how to find
the little white house
in the woods."

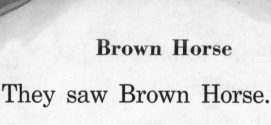

Brown Horse said, "I know
how to find the little white house.
Get on and ride.
Get on me, so!
And away we go
to the little white house
in the woods."

Up on Brown Horse went
Little Boy and Little Girl.
And up went all the animals.

"So here we go!"
said Brown Horse.
"Here we go
to the little white house
with the little red roof
and the little blue door."

At Home

Little Boy and Little Girl
and all the animals came
to the little house in the woods.

"Little House,"
said Brown Horse.
"Here are a boy and a girl.
They have no home.
They want a home."

"Come in! Come in!"
said the little white house.
"Come in and live here!"

"Thank you! We will!"
said Little Boy and Little Girl.
Then all the animals said,
"Good-by, Little Boy
and Little Girl.
We must go."

Little Boy
and Little Girl said,
"Good-by, Brown Horse.
Good-by, Gray Rabbit.
Good-by, Brown Hen.
Good-by, Red Rooster.
Good-by, Yellow Cat.
Good-by, Black Dog."

Then Little Boy
and Little Girl went
into the little white house
in the woods.
They live there now.

Which Is Right?

1. Jim and Judy like toys.
   Jim and Judy make hay.

2. Judy had a black and white cow.
   Jim had a birthday surprise.

3. Judy painted the animals.
   Jim looked at the airplanes.

4. The rooster went to the city.
   The horse went to school.

5. In the woods was a little house.
   On the farm was a pet store.

6. "Tags is a big gray rabbit,"
   said Jim.

   "Twinkle is my airplane cat,"
   said Judy.

Word List

The following list contains the 129 words introduced in *Tags and Twinkle*, primer of the *Today's Work-Play Books*. The 30 words introduced in *Come and Ride*, basal pre-primer, are repeated, making the total vocabulary of this book 159 words.

1.	27. can	47. know	67. little
2.	28. got	away	all
3.	into	48. they	68. but
4.	29. out	want	69.
5.	of	49.	70. city
6.	30. ran	50. big	71. looked
7.	31. not	up	saw
8. toys	have	51.	72. she
9.	32. happy	52. he	73.
10.	33. thank	painted	74.
11.	you	53. down	75. was
12.	34. what	no	76. where
13. a	see	54. good	home
make	35. did	55. too	77.
14. will	yes	56.	78.
15. wagon	36. oh	57.	79. bow-wow
16. for	37.	58. house	80. there
17. red	38. in	59. something	cat
18.	39. boys	eat	81.
19. birthday	girls	60.	82. Twinkle
surprises	40. played	61.	83. my
20. tomorrow	41.	62.	call
Jim's	42. cake	63. are	84.
21.	43.	64. white	85.
22. box	44. good-by	pilot	86. train
23. wheels	45. airplanes	65. man	87. put
24. on	46. with	66. going	88. had
25.	do		took
26. it			

89. cows	101. chickens	116.	133. woods
barn	yellow	117.	134.
90. some	102. pet	118.	135. find
91. hens	store	119.	136.
black	103. letter	120.	137. must
92. eggs	came	121. school	so
me	104. peep	122.	138. us
93. rooster	105. then	123.	139.
biggest	106. farmer's	124. Miss	140.
94. animal	wife	how	141. brown
cock-a-	107. now	125. blue	142.
doodle-doo	108.	126. play	143.
95. am	109. one	127. roof	144.
96. bigger	110. two	door	145.
than	rabbits	128. lives	146.
97.	111. gray	129.	147.
98. him	112. wanted	130. dog	148.
99. tell	113.	horses	149.
story	114.	131.	150.
100.	115.	132.	151.
			152.